LOVE 2B ME

CREATE DREAMY **DOODLES** and have **FUN** with
the FILL-IN PAGES. Then **DESIGN** an OUT-OF-THIS-WORLD
PROM DRESS before creating a **COMIC STRIP** of your **LIFE**.

·

With QUIZZES to share, **LISTS** to create and over
500 STICKERS to use wherever you want!

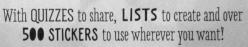

*make
believe
ideas*

ALL *about* ME

DRAW YOURSELF in the FRAME, and then FILL IN the info.

MY NAME: _____

I RATE MY NAME: /10

MY BIRTHDAY: _____

MY EYE COLOUR: _____

MY HAIR COLOUR: _____

Choose ONE NAME from each side of the HEART, then COMBINE these to create your CODE NAME.

MY CODE NAME:

_____ _____

Violet
Star   Liberty
Berry   Edie
Bear   Summer
Rose
Poppy
Zara   Frost

Sparkle
Valentine   Appleton
Diamond   Winter
Dazzle   Peardrop
Moon
Pickle

2

CIRCLE the **BIRTHSTONE** for the **MONTH** you were **BORN.**

JANUARY
Garnet

FEBRUARY
Amethyst

MARCH
Aquamarine

APRIL
Diamond

MAY
Emerald

JUNE
Pearl

JULY
Ruby

AUGUST
Peridot

SEPTEMBER
Sapphire

OCTOBER
Opal

NOVEMBER
Citrine

DECEMBER
Blue topaz

THE FIVE BEST THINGS ABOUT ME:

1 _____

2 _____

3 _____

4 _____

5 _____

THREE...

WORDS that BEST describe **ME**:

1 _____

2 _____

3 _____

NICKNAMES I've been **GIVEN**:

1 _____

2 _____

3 _____

Things I **LIKE** about **ME**:

1 _____

2 _____

3 _____

TOP TEN songs OF ALL TIME

1. _____
2. _____
3. _____
4. _____
5. _____
6. _____
7. _____
8. _____
9. _____
10. _____

WHAT KIND OF *snack* ARE YOU?

Are you a **STRAWBERRY CREAM**, a **COOL CARAMEL** or a **NUTTY CLUSTER**? FOLLOW the **FLOW** to FIND OUT.

START

| GOLD |
| SILVER |

| NEW BAG |
| NEW HAIR |

| WRITE A STORY |
| READ A BOOK |

| PLAY TO WIN |
| PLAY FOR FUN |

| HAPPY TO WAIT |
| WANT IT NOW! |

| WORK |
| PLAY |

| TV DRAMA |
| REALITY SHOW |

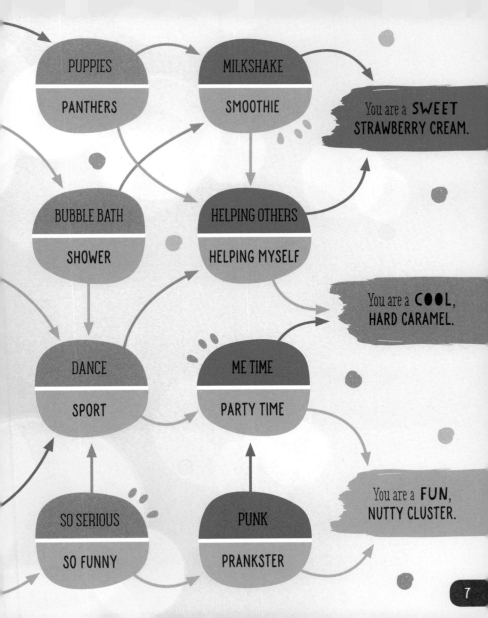

PUPPIES / PANTHERS

MILKSHAKE / SMOOTHIE

You are a **SWEET** STRAWBERRY CREAM.

BUBBLE BATH / SHOWER

HELPING OTHERS / HELPING MYSELF

You are a **COOL**, HARD CARAMEL.

DANCE / SPORT

ME TIME / PARTY TIME

SO SERIOUS / SO FUNNY

PUNK / PRANKSTER

You are a **FUN**, NUTTY CLUSTER.

BEEN THERE, DONE THAT!

☑ the **BOXES** for 'YES', 'ONE DAY I MIGHT', or 'I NEVER WANT TO!'

HAVE YOU EVER...	YES	ONE DAY I MIGHT	I NEVER WANT TO!
SEEN A CROCODILE?	☐	☐	☐
RIDDEN IN A HOT-AIR BALLOON?	☐	☐	☐
KNITTED A SCARF?	☐	☐	☐
CAPTAINED A SPORTS TEAM?	☐	☐	☐
WRITTEN A SONG?	☐	☐	☐
MADE YOUR OWN JEWELLERY?	☐	☐	☐
TRAINED A PUPPY?	☐	☐	☐
SAILED ON A YACHT?	☐	☐	☐
TALKED ON THE RADIO?	☐	☐	☐
MET A CELEBRITY?	☐	☐	☐
BEEN ON TV?	☐	☐	☐

THREE
GOALS
FOR THE NEXT...

WEEK

1 _____

2 _____

3 _____

MONTH

1 _____

2 _____

3 _____

YEAR

1 _____

2 _____

3 _____

FAMILY
▸▸▸▸ FACTS ◂◂◂◂

DRAW your **FAMILY** in the **FRAMES**, and then fill in the **INFO**.

NAME: _____

RELATION TO ME: _____

TWO WORDS THAT BEST DESCRIBE THEM:

1 _____

2 _____

NAME: _____

RELATION TO ME: _____

TWO WORDS THAT BEST DESCRIBE THEM:

1 _____

2 _____

NAME: _____

RELATION TO ME: _____

TWO WORDS THAT BEST DESCRIBE THEM:

1 _____

2 _____

NAME: _____

RELATION TO ME: _____

TWO WORDS THAT BEST DESCRIBE THEM:

1 _____

2 _____

NAME: _____

RELATION TO ME: _____

TWO WORDS THAT BEST DESCRIBE THEM:

1 _____

2 _____

OODLES OF
doodles

TRANSFORM the **DOODLES** into works of ART by adding **ARMS**, **LEGS**, **FACES**, **WHEELS**, **WIGGLES** or whatever you want!

ME, ME, ME

WRITE your NAME starting with a
TINY LETTER, then make the letters
BIGGER AND
BIGGER!
Keep WRITING your NAME until
the PAGE is FULL.

WILL I EVER?

	I HOPE SO	MAYBE	NO WAY!
WRITE A NOVEL	☐	☐	☐
BE A YOUTUBE STAR	☐	☐	☐
RUN A MARATHON	☐	☐	☐
OWN A HORSE	☐	☐	☐
VISIT THE NORTH POLE	☐	☐	☐
GO TO SPACE	☐	☐	☐
LIVE ON A FARM	☐	☐	☐
JOIN A CHOIR	☐	☐	☐
LEARN ANOTHER LANGUAGE	☐	☐	☐
APPEAR ON A REALITY SHOW	☐	☐	☐
FLY AN AEROPLANE	☐	☐	☐
HAVE A #1 HIT	☐	☐	☐

MY best...

SPORTING achievement

_____

_____

AWARD or PRIZE

_____

_____

PERFORMANCE on STAGE

_____

_____

PERSONALITY TRAIT

_____

_____

SCHOOL GRADE

_____

HABIT

_____

_____

SKILL or TALENT

_____

_____

PRETTY
PORTRAITS

DRAW a **SELF PORTRAIT**.

DRAW a PORTRAIT of your **BFF**.

Name GAME

Do any of the WORDS MATCH?

WOULD YOU RATHER...

CIRCLE your CHOICES!

JOIN A BAND	**OR**	A CIRCUS?
LIVE IN A CAVE	**OR**	A TREEHOUSE?
DYE YOUR HAIR PINK	**OR**	PAINT YOUR NAILS BLACK?
HOLD A SLIMY SLUG	**OR**	A HAIRY SPIDER?
DIVE INTO A POOL OF JELLY	**OR**	A POOL OF CUSTARD?
RUN THROUGH MUD	**OR**	SIT ON GRAVEL?
WEAR A CLOWN'S NOSE	**OR**	CLOWN'S SHOES?
HAVE THREE BROTHERS	**OR**	THREE SISTERS?
ONLY HAVE SHOWERS	**OR**	ONLY HAVE BATHS?
EAT CEREAL WITHOUT MILK	**OR**	TOAST WITHOUT BUTTER?

MY dream HOME

19

Star SEARCH

Find the **CELEBRITY WORDS** in the GRID.

award · fame · limo · microphone
movie · music · premiere · superstar

e	b	c	d	r	b	z	a	l	w	a	v
y	m	s	q	p	f	a	w	m	s	u	i
l	i	m	o	v	r	w	t	i	a	p	d
f	c	y	i	m	j	a	o	p	e	s	i
v	r	y	u	u	i	r	l	k	r	u	r
i	o	z	d	s	q	d	p	m	z	p	s
a	p	i	o	i	b	a	f	a	m	e	t
r	h	g	c	c	u	i	p	v	a	r	r
n	o	f	m	i	r	w	f	g	t	s	a
l	n	t	m	o	v	i	e	i	e	t	i
o	e	k	l	x	o	d	l	h	a	a	e
u	h	p	r	p	r	e	m	i	e	r	e

3 THINGS
I'D DO IF...

I were INVISIBLE

1 _____

2 _____

3 _____

I could FLY

1 _____

2 _____

3 _____

I could TIME TRAVEL

1 _____

2 _____

3 _____

FRIENDSHIP SURVEY

Write **YOUR** and a FRIEND'S name at the top of the **SURVEY**, and then answer the **QUESTIONS** for each other.

NAMES:

CUPCAKE OR MARSHMALLOW?		
BOARD GAME OR VIDEO GAME?		
EGGS OR BACON?		
GYMNASTICS OR FOOTBALL?		
CARROTS OR PEAS?		
BLUE OR YELLOW?		
PEANUT BUTTER OR JAM?		
CALL OR MESSAGE?		
PLANE OR CRUISE SHIP?		
BICYCLE OR SCOOTER?		
PAINTING OR DRAWING?		
PARTY OR FANCY MEAL?		

Now, **CHECK** your **ANSWERS** to see how well you **KNOW** each other!

PICK A PET

CAT

You are strong and independent and happy chilling on your own or with friends. You are an artistic person and you like nothing better than lying in the sun with some good music or a fantastic book!

You're bright, perky and full of fun but you do like your alone-time too! You're a night owl and can't stand early mornings. Your friends love your quirky sense of humour and inner determination.

HAMSTER

RABBIT

You're friendly, fun and full of energy! You might be small, but your individual personality always leaves a big impression. Your friends love your adorable smile and kind nature.

You're an amazing friend! You're gentle, kind and very loyal. You're fun-loving and inquisitive and enjoy learning new things. You have endless energy so can be hard to keep up with sometimes!

DOG

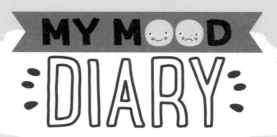

MY MOOD DIARY

DRAW an **EMOJI** that best **DESCRIBES** how you FEEL every day for a **WEEK**.

MONDAY

TUESDAY

WEDNESDAY

THURSDAY

FRIDAY

SATURDAY

SUNDAY

Tasty

OR TERRIBLE?

✓ the **BOX** for FOODS you LOVE and ✗ the **BOX** for FOODS you think are **GROSS!**

COCONUT	☐	APRICOTS	☐
SPINACH	☐	SOUR SWEETS	☐
CREAM CHEESE	☐	PEANUT BUTTER	☐
ICED TEA	☐	TUNA PIZZA	☐
BROCCOLI	☐	HOT MILK	☐
CHERRY COLA	☐	SCRAMBLED EGGS	☐
CINNAMON COOKIES	☐	BLUE CHEESE	☐
MARZIPAN	☐	DARK CHOCOLATE	☐
MINT ICE CREAM	☐	BRUSSELS SPROUTS	☐
MASHED POTATOES	☐	MUSHROOMS	☐
BEETROOT	☐	CELERY	☐
TOMATOES	☐	MARSHMALLOWS	☐

WHAT'S YOUR SFQ?

Everyone has something **SPECIAL** to bring to a **FRIENDSHIP**: their **SFQ**, or "SPECIAL FRIENDSHIP QUALITY." Circle **FIVE WORDS** that best **DESCRIBE** you, and then find out your **SFQ**.

ENERGETIC

GENTLE

OUTRAGEOUS

SMART

CREATIVE

CONFIDENT

FUNNY

LOVING

CAREFUL

SPORTY

OPINIONATED

THOUGHTFUL

FOCUSSED

LOUD

SHY

CAUTIOUS

BRAVE

QUIET

MAINLY GREEN

You are sensitive and always seem to know the right thing to say. You make friends for life and will be the first to come running if a friend needs help or support.

MAINLY PINK

You're fun to be around, and you love the thrill of adventure. You're not afraid to say what you think, and your positive outlook means that you will not be too upset if people disagree with you!

MAINLY BLUE

Though you might not always show it, your friendship runs deep. You think things through and once you've made up your mind, you rarely change it. You have a competitive side, which means you want the best for you and your friends.

REALLY RANDOM LIST

WHAT'S THE MOST RANDOM...

MEAL YOU'VE EATEN? _____

HAIRSTYLE YOU'VE SEEN? _____

SHOES YOU'VE WORN? _____

YOUTUBE CHANNEL YOU'VE WATCHED? _____

NICKNAME YOU'VE BEEN GIVEN? _____

PLACE YOU'VE FALLEN ASLEEP? _____

ICE-CREAM FLAVOUR YOU'VE EATEN? _____

SONG YOU'VE HEARD? _____

CLOTHES COMBINATION YOU'VE SEEN? _____

TOURIST ATTRACTION YOU'VE BEEN TO? _____

FILM YOU'VE WATCHED? _____

EMAIL ADDRESS YOU'VE HAD? _____

BOOK YOU'VE READ? _____

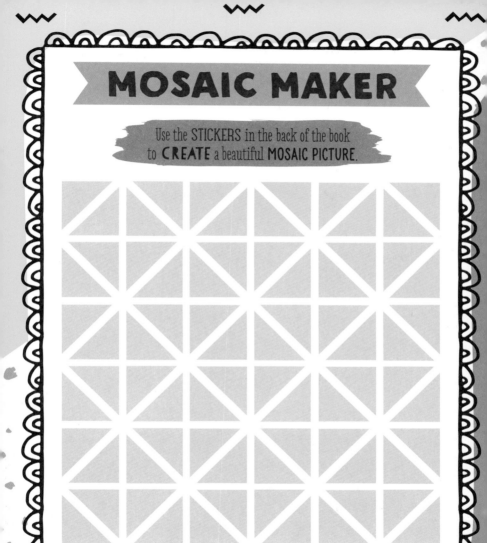

MOSAIC MAKER

Use the STICKERS in the back of the book
to **CREATE** a beautiful **MOSAIC PICTURE**.

SWEET search

Fill the **HEARTS** with the **NAMES** of people who are **SPECIAL** to you.

Now, fill the **GRID** with these **NAMES**. Try to **LINK** the names **TOGETHER** like a CROSSWORD PUZZLE and then fill in the **BLANKS** with RANDOM LETTERS. Finally, CHALLENGE a LOVED ONE to **FIND** all the NAMES in the **WORDSEARCH**.

SIX-WORD *reviews*

THINK OF SIX WORDS TO DESCRIBE THE LAST...

FILM YOU SAW   TITLE: _____

1 _____   4 _____

2 _____   5 _____

3 _____   6 _____

BOOK YOU READ   TITLE: _____

1 _____   4 _____

2 _____   5 _____

3 _____   6 _____

SONG YOU HEARD NAME: _____

1 _____   4 _____

2 _____   5 _____

3 _____   6 _____

SHOW YOU SAW NAME: _____

1 _____   4 _____

2 _____   5 _____

3 _____   6 _____

FOOD YOU ATE NAME: _____

1 _____   4 _____

2 _____   5 _____

3 _____   6 _____

ON A SCALE OF
ONE TO TEN

this is how much I'd like to . . .

FLY TO THE MOON /10

HAVE MY OWN YOUTUBE CHANNEL /10

HAVE A BEDROOM MAKEOVER /10

TRAIN TO BE A TOP CHEF /10

MAKE SLIME WITH KARINA GARCIA /10

NEVER HAVE TO CUT MY TOENAILS /10

LIVE TO BE 200 YEARS OLD /10

BE A SPIDER FOR A DAY /10

SING A DUET WITH ARIANA GRANDE /10

BE TEN YEARS OLDER FOR A DAY /10

:FOOD:
FAVOURITES

BREAKFAST

_____

LUNCH

_____

DINNER

_____

DESSERT

_____

WRITE the names of **EIGHT** people you would INVITE to your **DREAM DINNER PARTY**.

1 _____

2 _____

3 _____

4 _____

5 _____

6 _____

7 _____

8 _____

WHAT DOES YOUR
HANDWRITING
SAY ABOUT YOU?

SMALL AND NEAT
You are loyal
and thoughtful.
A true BFF!

BIG
YOU ARE OUTGOING AND
FUN TO BE AROUND.
YOU ALWAYS MAKE
YOUR FRIENDS LAUGH!

UPRIGHT
You are a
natural leader and
a life-long friend
to people you love.

Write your name here:

SLANTING FORWARDS
*You are trusting
and kind. You love
spending time
with your friends.*

SLANTING BACKWARDS
You can take a while to
open up to people, but
once you do, you're a
friend for life!

SWIRLY
You are imaginative
and creative.
You always have
fun stories to tell.

MY MINI
MANICURE

DRAW around your FINGERTIPS, and then design an **OUTRAGEOUS MANICURE** for your NAILS.

Fantasy

►►►► FORTUNE COOKIES ◄◄◄◄

1 Take the number of letters in your first name (this must be your full name, not a nickname). Then work out what number day of the week it is and add these two numbers together. So, if your name is Ashley and it is Tuesday, your number is: 6 + 2 = 8.

2 Starting in the nibbled segment of the "Talent" cookie, move clockwise around the circle, taking the same number of steps as your number. This will tell you what you will be famous for.

3 The "Talent" segment you land on will have a number. Move onto the "City" cookie, and using that number, start at the nibbled segment and work your way around to see where you will live.

4 Continue in the same way to find out your future home!

TALENT

12 MUSICIAN
4 DANCER
WRITER
10
ACTOR
6
ARTIST
8

CITY

12 NEW YORK
PARIS 4
SYDNEY
10
LOS ANGELES
6
LONDON
8

HOME

MANSION
PALACE
CASTLE
PENTHOUSE
WINDMILL

MY TALENT: _____

MY CITY: _____

MY HOME: _____

39

3 WISHES

If you could have **THREE WISHES**, what would they be?

1 _____
_____
_____

2 _____
_____
_____

3 _____
_____
_____
_____

WOULD YOU RATHER...

CIRCLE your CHOICES!

LEARN TO SURF	OR	LEARN TO SKI?
HAVE £20 NOW	OR	£100 IN A YEAR?
WEAR BOOTS ON THE BEACH	OR	FLIP-FLOPS IN THE SNOW?
HAVE NO TV FOR A YEAR	OR	NO GAMES FOR A YEAR?
BE A FAMOUS SINGER	OR	A FAMOUS WRITER?
WORK IN A SCHOOL	OR	IN A HOSPITAL?
MILK A COW	OR	MUCK OUT A STABLE?
VISIT THE PAST	OR	VISIT THE FUTURE?
RIDE A HORSE	OR	RIDE A UNICYCLE?
BE A TV STAR FOR A DAY	OR	A ROCK STAR FOR A DAY?

Star SWAP

If you could be any of these PEOPLE for a DAY, who would you choose? CIRCLE your CHOICE.

A film star

A YouTube star

A pop star

A TV star

A member of the British royal family

A world record holder

An author

A sports star

An historical figure

5 THINGS THAT...

CAN MAKE MY DAY:

1. _____
2. _____
3. _____
4. _____
5. _____

CAN MAKE ME LAUGH:

1. _____
2. _____
3. _____
4. _____
5. _____

I CAN DO TO IMPROVE A FRIEND'S DAY:

1.
2.
3.
4.
5.

WILL I EVER?

	I HOPE SO	MAYBE	NO WAY!
SWIM TO THE BOTTOM OF THE OCEAN	☐	☐	☐
SLEEP IN AN IGLOO	☐	☐	☐
CAPTAIN A SHIP	☐	☐	☐
MEET A ROYAL	☐	☐	☐
CLIMB A MOUNTAIN	☐	☐	☐
BREAK A WORLD RECORD	☐	☐	☐
TAKE A PARACHUTE JUMP	☐	☐	☐
CAMP IN THE DESERT	☐	☐	☐
TREK THROUGH A RAINFOREST	☐	☐	☐
SKI DOWN A MOUNTAIN	☐	☐	☐
WIN A NOBEL PRIZE	☐	☐	☐
GO BUNGEE JUMPING	☐	☐	☐

FUTURE HOME

designer

DESIGN a HOUSE
for the year 3000.

WILL YOU BE A STAR?

Answer the **QUESTIONS** and COLOUR a **SQUARE** for each POINT you score. When you have answered all the questions, find the **STAR** you are CLOSEST to for your RESULT.

START HERE

1 HAVE YOU EVER ENTERED A TALENT SHOW?
Yes (2)
Yes, and I won! (3)
No way! (0)

2 DO YOU PRACTICE YOUR AUTOGRAPH?
All the time (3)
Occasionally (2)
Never (0)

You are destined to excel out of the limelight.

3 HOW DO YOU HANDLE CRITICISM?
I get upset (1)
I work hard to prove it wrong (2)
I take it to heart and try to improve (3)

4 DO YOU DRESS TO...
be comfortable? (1)
stand out? (3)
impress your friends? (2)

You have a foot on the fame ladder, but you need to work harder if you want to shine!

46

7 DO YOU LOVE TO LEARN NEW SKILLS?
Yes, the more the better (3)
Only if I'm interested (2)
Not really (0)

It looks like you've got what it takes to be a star!

6 IF YOU WERE PAPPED, WOULD YOU...
cover your face? (0)
strike a pose? (2)
pretend to be shocked but pose at the same time? (3)

8
WHAT'S THE BEST REWARD FOR DOING A GOOD PERFORMANCE?
Applause (3)
Praise (2)
Money (1)

Fame may come knocking on your door, but will you open it?

5 DO YOU BELIEVE YOU HAVE A UNIQUE TALENT?
Not really (0)
Maybe not unique, but I'm definitely talented (2)
Absolutely (3)

With your style and attitude, you could be a superstar!

3 FRIENDS
I WOULD...

share a **HOUSE** with:

1 _____

2 _____

3 _____

start a **BAND** with:

1 _____

2 _____

3 _____

run a **MARATHON** with:

1 _____

2 _____

3 _____

REALLY RANDOM LIST

WHAT'S THE MOST RANDOM...

THING YOU'VE WORN IN YOUR HAIR? _____

PRESENT YOU'VE GIVEN? _____

PRESENT YOU'VE RECEIVED? _____

THING UNDER YOUR BED? _____

THING YOU'VE SEEN A PET WEARING? _____

DANCE YOU'VE SEEN? _____

HAIR COLOUR YOU'VE SEEN? _____

BREAKFAST YOU'VE HAD? _____

VEHICLE YOU'VE BEEN IN? _____

HOMEWORK YOU'VE BEEN GIVEN? _____

SANDWICH YOU'VE MADE? _____

FANCY DRESS COSTUME YOU'VE WORN? _____

DREAM YOU'VE HAD? _____

TOP TUNE

WRITE the **LYRICS** to your **FAVOURITE SONG** here.

TITLE: _____

_____
_____
_____
_____
_____
_____
_____
_____
_____
_____
_____
_____
_____

_____
_____
_____
_____
_____
_____
_____
_____
_____
_____
_____
_____
_____

squiggles

DRAW SQUIGGLES and **LOOPS** across the page, and then **COLOUR** in the **SHAPES** you've made.

House HUNT

Find the **HOUSEHOLD ITEMS** in the GRID.

bath | bed | chair | curtains
desk | fridge | table | television

h	p	g	r	l	x	j	x	b	a	t	h
m	t	a	b	l	e	u	i	e	s	k	q
o	w	c	h	r	s	l	l	a	m	d	i
p	t	h	q	d	f	r	i	d	g	e	u
r	c	a	d	s	v	b	w	z	z	s	u
t	n	i	m	e	j	x	d	e	m	k	x
w	l	r	b	f	z	a	e	p	o	b	v
x	t	e	l	e	v	i	s	i	o	n	y
l	n	s	f	c	u	r	t	a	i	n	s
w	b	e	k	s	r	q	b	z	i	x	d
n	r	a	b	c	m	w	e	k	x	o	v
l	g	d	r	s	y	d	d	u	c	l	p

52

ON A SCALE OF
ONE TO TEN

this is how much I'd like to . . .

FLY A HELICOPTER /10

LIVE IN A WINDMILL /10

BE INVISIBLE FOR A DAY /10

DYE MY HAIR BLUE /10

DIRECT MY OWN FILM /10

SING ON STAGE /10

BE A FIREFIGHTER /10

GO BACK IN TIME /10

CAMP IN A FOREST /10

SKI DOWN A MOUNTAIN /10

TOP 10

BOOKS I'VE READ

1 _____

2 _____

3 _____

4 _____

5 _____

6 _____

7 _____

8 _____

9 _____

10 _____

FASHION
jumble

REARRANGE the letters to reveal FOUR things you'd find in a **HAIR SALON**.

D E
R R Y

_____

S R O S
S I C S

_____

O R M
I R R

_____

R E L
L O R S

_____

Find the **THREE** items of **CLOTHING** JUMBLED up in this SEQUENCE. All the **LETTERS** are in the **CORRECT** order.

J S A O J C E C A K N K E S T

1 ___ ___ ___ ___ ___

2 ___ ___ ___ ___ ___ ___

3 ___ ___ ___ ___ ___

FRIENDSHIP SURVEY

Write **YOUR** and a FRIEND'S name at the top of the **SURVEY**, then answer the **QUESTIONS** for each other.

NAMES:

SWEETCORN OR BROCCOLI?		
TOWN OR COUNTRY?		
THEATRE OR CINEMA?		
HOT TUB OR SWIMMING POOL?		
RICH OR FAMOUS?		
BREAKFAST OR BRUNCH?		
VLOGGER OR DJ?		
LEARN FRENCH OR GERMAN?		
HORSE OR PONY?		
KITTEN OR PUPPY?		
SWIMMING OR TENNIS?		
WALK OR RUN?		

Now, **CHECK** your **ANSWERS** to see how well you **KNOW** each other!

NAME-A-PUP

Think of CUTE NAMES for the PUPPIES.

RANDOM *Decision* MAKER

CLOSE your eyes, then **SWIRL** your finger in the air and let it **LAND** anywhere on the page. DECISION MADE!

Try a new hairstyle

Finish your homework

Tidy your bedroom

Invent a new dance

Write a happy song

Read a new book

Write a short story

Draw a cartoon character

Learn a new skill

3 ACHIEVEMENTS

Think of **THREE** achievements that have made you feel PROUD. **WRITE** them here, and then **DRAW** them in the BOXES.

1 _____

_____

_____

_____

2 _____

_____

_____

_____

3 _____

_____

_____

_____

HAIR
STUDIO

Doodle **PARTY-PERFECT HAIRSTYLES** on the models.

DREAM
PARTY

WHO would you INVITE?

STARS and CELEBRITIES

1 _____

2 _____

3 _____

4 _____

5 _____

6 _____

7 _____

8 _____

PEOPLE from the PAST

1 _____

2 _____

3 _____

4 _____

5 _____

6 _____

7 _____

8 _____

3 FRIENDS WHO...

I've **KNOWN** the **LONGEST**:

1 _____

2 _____

3 _____

make me **LAUGH**:

1 _____

2 _____

3 _____

give great **ADVICE**:

1 _____

2 _____

3 _____

WHAT KIND OF *dessert* ARE YOU?

FOLLOW the **FLOW** to **FIND OUT.**

START

- HOT WEATHER
- COLD WEATHER

- SPORTS CLASS
- ENGLISH CLASS

- HANG AT HOME
- STAY OUT

- ACTRESS
- DOCTOR

- CLOSE FRIENDS
- EVERYONE'S PAL

- GIVING GIFTS
- RECEIVING GIFTS

BEACH

MOUNTAIN

ICE CREAM

You are a fun-loving free spirit and you're always the life and soul of a party. You have a flair for anything artistic or creative and people love to listen to your cool conversation.

SINGING

DANCING

APPLE PIE

You are a sweet-hearted soul and you value your family and friends above anything. You can be traditional, but you are always great fun to be around – especially during the holidays!

HOMEMADE

FAST FOOD

LAYERED CAKE

Your soft-heartedness makes you everyone's favourite friend. You are the super-girly queen of slumber parties – nobody arranges a midnight feast like you!

PASTEL COLOURS

BRIGHT COLOURS

FRUIT SALAD

You are an adventurous character with a great sense of humour. You are a little bit of a clown – but everyone loves you for it.

Prom NIGHT

DESIGN an OUTFIT for a PROM NIGHT in SPACE.

WOULD YOU RATHER...

CIRCLE your CHOICES!

DRINK A BROCCOLI SMOOTHIE	**OR**	A CHEESE MILKSHAKE?
BE INVISIBLE FOR A DAY	**OR**	FAMOUS FOR A DAY?
LIVE ON A SPACE STATION	**OR**	IN A SUBMARINE?
BE THE STAR OF A SHOW	**OR**	THE DIRECTOR?
RECEIVE ART SUPPLIES	**OR**	MUSIC CONCERT TICKETS?
WRITE A BEST-SELLING BOOK	**OR**	HAVE A #1 SONG?
SIT IN A BATH OF SLIME	**OR**	PASTA SAUCE?
DRINK SOUP WITH A STRAW	**OR**	DRINK COLA FROM A BOWL?
BE AN ONLY CHILD	**OR**	A TRIPLET?
WEAR YOUR CLOTHES INSIDE OUT	**OR**	BACK TO FRONT?

3 THINGS
TO DO ON A...

SUNNY day

1 _____

2 _____

3 _____

RAINY day

1 _____

2 _____

3 _____

SNOWY day

1 _____

2 _____

3 _____

TOP 10

TREATS AND SNACKS

1 _____

2 _____

3 _____

4 _____

5 _____

6 _____

7 _____

8 _____

9 _____

10 _____

DESIGNER

DESIGN a **T-SHIRT** for a **SUMMER HOLIDAY**.

LOTS OF choices

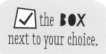

☑ the **BOX** next to your choice.

MORNINGS:
- UP EARLY ☐
- SLEEP IN ☐

HAIR:
- SHORT AND NEAT ☐
- LONG AND WAVY ☐

SPORTS:
- ON THE TEAM ☐
- CHEERLEADING ☐

SEASONS:
- SUMMER ☐
- WINTER ☐

FAST FOOD:
- PIZZA ☐
- BURGER ☐

AT NIGHT:
- READ IN BED ☐
- STRAIGHT TO SLEEP ☐

MY ROOM:
- PERSONAL SPACE ☐
- SOCIAL PLACE ☐

SWIMMING POOL:
- LAPS ☐
- LILO ☐

▶▶▶▶ IF YOU WERE A ◀◀◀◀
MILLIONARE

IMAGINE you are a **MILLIONARE** and then fill in the INFO.

FRIEND'S NAME: _____

TWO THINGS YOU WOULD BUY THEM:

1 _____

2 _____

SOMETHING YOU WOULD GIVE THEM THAT MONEY CANNOT BUY:

3 _____

FRIEND'S NAME: _____

TWO THINGS YOU WOULD BUY THEM:

1 _____

2 _____

SOMETHING YOU WOULD GIVE THEM THAT MONEY CANNOT BUY:

3 _____

FRIEND'S NAME: _____

TWO THINGS YOU WOULD BUY THEM:

1 _____

2 _____

SOMETHING YOU WOULD GIVE THEM THAT MONEY CANNOT BUY:

3 _____

FRIEND'S NAME: _____

TWO THINGS YOU WOULD BUY THEM:

1 _____

2 _____

SOMETHING YOU WOULD GIVE THEM THAT MONEY CANNOT BUY:

3 _____

THREE CHARITIES YOU WOULD DONATE TO:

1 _____

2 _____

3 _____

BEEN THERE, DONE THAT!

☑ the **BOXES** for 'YES', 'ONE DAY I MIGHT', or 'I NEVER WANT TO!'

HAVE YOU EVER...	YES	ONE DAY I MIGHT	I NEVER WANT TO!
LIVED IN ANOTHER COUNTRY?	☐	☐	☐
KEPT A PET SNAKE?	☐	☐	☐
TAKEN A DANCE CLASS?	☐	☐	☐
PERFORMED IN A PLAY?	☐	☐	☐
BEEN SCUBA DIVING?	☐	☐	☐
SPENT THE NIGHT IN A TENT?	☐	☐	☐
INVENTED A NEW MILKSHAKE FLAVOUR?	☐	☐	☐
BEEN TO A WATER PARK?	☐	☐	☐
SEEN THE NORTHERN LIGHTS?	☐	☐	☐
SWUM IN A LAKE?	☐	☐	☐
HIKED ON A GLACIER?	☐	☐	☐

LETTER LINKS

Write ten **GIRLS'** names in the LEFT column and ten **BOYS'** names in the RIGHT column. The **FIRST** letter of each **BOY'S** name must be the **LAST** letter of the **GIRL'S** name next to it.

1 _____

2 _____

3 _____

4 _____

5 _____

6 _____

7 _____

8 _____

9 _____

10 _____

1 _____

2 _____

3 _____

4 _____

5 _____

6 _____

7 _____

8 _____

9 _____

10 _____

THE
:view:
FROM MY WINDOW

DRAW what you SEE
from your bedroom **WINDOW**.

REALLY RANDOM LIST

WHAT'S THE MOST RANDOM...

PET YOU'VE WANTED? _____

ITEM IN YOUR SCHOOL LOCKER? _____

PIZZA TOPPING YOU'VE HEARD OF? _____

SHOW YOU'VE SEEN? _____

COMPETITION YOU'VE ENTERED? _____

SHOP IN YOUR TOWN? _____

NICKNAME YOU'VE GIVEN SOMEONE? _____

TALENT YOU HAVE? _____

THING IN YOUR WARDROBE? _____

OBJECT IN YOUR ROOM? _____

ICE-CREAM TOPPING YOU'VE EATEN? _____

STORY YOU'VE HEARD? _____

THING YOU'VE PUT ON A WISH LIST? _____

TOWN OR COUNTRY

ANSWER the **QUESTIONS** and work your way around the **WHEEL** to discover your **TOWN** or COUNTRY brain-mix. **EXCITEMENT** and **GLAMOUR**, or **FRESH AIR** and FREEDOM – it all adds up to **100%** you!

1 IF YOU HAD A CHOICE, WOULD YOU RATHER TRAVEL BY ...

TAXI? (Move around 5)
BUS? (Move around 2)
HORSEBACK? (Move around 0)

2 WHICH IS THE BEST?

BALLET (Move around 2)
BARN DANCE (Move around 0)
STREET DANCE (Move around 5)

4 IF YOU HAD A CHOICE, WOULD YOU RATHER LIVE IN ...

A WINDMILL? (Move around 0)
A PENTHOUSE? (Move around 5)
A HOUSEBOAT? (Move around 2)

5 WHICH OF THESE ACTIVITIES DO YOU ENJOY THE MOST?

SWIMMING (Move around 2)
SHOPPING (Move around 5)
HIKING (Move around 0)

Start at the heart

WRITE your **BRAIN-MIX** here:

_____ % COUNTRY   _____ % TOWN

I LOVE LISTS

BOOKS I plan to READ:

1. _____
2. _____
3. _____
4. _____
5. _____
6. _____
7. _____
8. _____

FILMS I plan to WATCH:

1. _____
2. _____
3. _____
4. _____
5. _____
6. _____
7. _____
8. _____

LOVE IT
OR LEAVE IT

CIRCLE your CHOICES!

COLA	OR	JUICE?
PENCILS	OR	PENS?
STRAIGHTENERS	OR	HAIRDRYER?
TV	OR	INTERNET?
BOOKS	OR	PARTIES?
CHAIRS	OR	TABLES?
QUILT	OR	PILLOWS?
CHOCOLATE	OR	SWEETS?
HATS	OR	SCARVES?
SWEET	OR	SAVOURY?

EMOJI MANIA

Fruity FINDS

apple · banana · blueberry · grape · melon · orange · peach · strawberry

i	u	z	i	s	k	s	a	p	p	l	e
n	l	x	f	r	x	p	e	a	c	h	f
y	i	r	z	y	s	u	r	d	a	i	k
m	u	l	c	r	t	g	r	a	p	e	f
e	g	j	v	w	r	y	y	h	b	f	r
l	a	y	q	b	a	n	a	n	a	g	r
o	p	k	h	d	w	f	o	c	l	f	p
n	b	l	u	e	b	e	r	r	y	k	m
d	e	m	y	v	e	d	a	s	d	g	n
s	y	h	s	f	r	r	n	u	z	v	b
z	r	o	w	x	r	x	g	p	l	v	x
q	h	r	k	j	y	m	e	s	x	r	w

IF I RULED THE
WORLD

THREE LAWS I would write:

1. _____

2. _____

3. _____

THREE things I would BAN:

1. _____

2. _____

3. _____

THREE things I would BUILD:

1. _____

2. _____

3. _____

Celebrity BFF

Of all the **FAMOUS** people and CELEBRITIES
on the planet, who would you **CHOOSE** to ...

HELP WITH YOUR SCIENCE HOMEWORK?

TEACH YOU TO DANCE?

TEACH YOU TO DRIVE?

HELP YOU TRAIN FOR A MARATHON?

DECORATE YOUR ROOM?

SHARE A ROOM WITH?

TEACH YOU TO SING?

GO ON HOLIDAY WITH?

PLAN A BIRTHDAY PARTY WITH?

GO CAMPING WITH?

THE **5** **BEST** THINGS ABOUT...

Write the **NAME** of a **FRIEND** at the top of each page.
Then write FIVE things you **LOVE** about them.

NAME: _____

1 _____

2 _____

3 _____

4 _____

5 _____

THE **5** **BEST**
THINGS ABOUT...

NAME:

1 _____

2 _____

3 _____

4 _____

5 _____

REALLY RANDOM LIST

WHAT'S THE MOST RANDOM...

MESSAGE YOU'VE RECEIVED?

BOOK YOU'VE READ?

RINGTONE YOU'VE HEARD?

COLOUR YOU'VE PAINTED YOUR NAILS?

THING YOU'VE WORN TO A PARTY?

EARRINGS YOU'VE SEEN?

DAY OUT YOU'VE HAD?

HAT YOU'VE WORN?

THING YOU'VE BOUGHT YOURSELF?

SLEEPOVER GAME YOU'VE PLAYED?

ANIMAL YOU'VE HELD?

SHOP YOU'VE BEEN IN?

DAYDREAM YOU'VE HAD?

PRETTY PETALS

Use the STICKERS in the back of the book
to **CREATE** a beautiful vase of **FLOWERS**.

Fancy
LETTERS

Keep **WRITING** your NAME in FANCY letters until the PAGE is **FULL**.

TOP 10

FRUITS AND VEGETABLES:

1. _____
2. _____
3. _____
4. _____
5. _____
6. _____
7. _____
8. _____
9. _____
10. _____

CHOCOLATES AND SWEETS:

1. _____
2. _____
3. _____
4. _____
5. _____
6. _____
7. _____
8. _____
9. _____
10. _____

FRIEND
▶▶▶ FACTS ◀◀◀

DRAW your **BFFs** in the FRAMES, and then **FILL IN** the info.

NAME: _____

WE'VE BEEN FRIENDS FOR: _____

TWO THINGS I LIKE ABOUT THEM:

1 _____

2 _____

NAME: _____

WE'VE BEEN FRIENDS FOR: _____

TWO THINGS I LIKE ABOUT THEM:

1 _____

2 _____

NAME: _____

WE'VE BEEN FRIENDS FOR: _____

TWO THINGS I LIKE ABOUT THEM:

1 _____

2 _____

NAME: _____

WE'VE BEEN FRIENDS FOR: _____

TWO THINGS I LIKE ABOUT THEM:

1 _____

2 _____

NAME: _____

WE'VE BEEN FRIENDS FOR: _____

TWO THINGS I LIKE ABOUT THEM:

1 _____

2 _____

9 FAMOUS PEOPLE
I'D LIKE TO MEET

THREE LIVING

1 _____

2 _____

3 _____

THREE **NOT LIVING**

1 _____

2 _____

3 _____

THREE FICTIONAL

1 _____

2 _____

3 _____

LOL!

DESCRIBE the FUNNIEST thing you ever SAW.

MY AMAZING
BEDROOM

DRAW a plan of your **BEDROOM** here!

FRIENDSHIP SURVEY

Write **YOUR** and a **FRIEND'S** name at the top of the **SURVEY**, then answer the **QUESTIONS** for each other.

NAMES:		
VANILLA OR MINT ICE CREAM?		
TOMATO SAUCE OR MUSTARD?		
BREAD OR CRACKERS?		
POP OR R&B?		
ICE-SKATING OR BOWLING?		
BURGER OR HOT DOG?		
ORANGE OR GRAPE JUICE?		
BOOK OR MAGAZINE?		
SLIMY OR SQUISHY?		
GREEN OR PURPLE?		
MUSIC OR COMEDY SHOW?		
SUPERHERO OR VILLAIN?		

Now, **CHECK** your **ANSWERS** to see how well you **KNOW** each other!

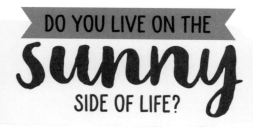

DO YOU LIVE ON THE *sunny* SIDE OF LIFE?

ANSWER the QUESTIONS, then total your As, Bs, and Cs.

1 IT'S YOUR BIRTHDAY AND ONLY TWO CARDS HAVE ARRIVED IN THE POST. WHAT'S YOUR TAKE?

A. Loads more cards will arrive tomorrow.
B. It's OK, birthdays aren't that important.
C. Practically everyone forgot.

2 YOUR BEST FRIEND IS GOING TO DISNEY WORLD FOR HER BIRTHDAY. SHE'S SO EXCITED. HOW DO YOU FEEL?

A. Pumped for your pal. You can't wait to hear all about it when she gets back.
B. Pleased she'll have a nice birthday.
C. Really jealous that you're not going.

3 YOU VISIT THE SHOPPING CENTRE AND THE CAR PARK IS NEARLY FULL. DOES THIS MEAN . . .

A. it's more likely all your friends will be there?
B. it's a regular Saturday?
C. the place will be crowded and all the best sale items will be sold out?

4 YOU COME THIRD IN THE SCHOOL ART COMPETITION. ARE YOU . . .

A. determined to do better next year and win?
B. happy to be in the top three?
C. convinced the winner must have got help to be that good?

5 YOU FIND 50p ON THE PAVEMENT. IS THIS . . .

A. enough to buy a treat for you and your best friend?
B. worth picking up and putting in your piggy bank?
C. not even enough to buy a soda?

6 YOUR MUM IS TAKING YOU AND YOUR FRIENDS BOWLING. IS THIS . . .

A. a chance for all your mates to see what a great mum you've got?
B. something very nice of her to do?
C. bound to end in total embarrassment?

MAINLY As

Wow! You certainly love to live in the sun. You have a great positive attitude – but don't worry if you feel sad sometimes: it's only natural!

MAINLY Bs

You certainly don't live your life in the clouds, but you're not basking in the sun either. You have an easygoing, balanced attitude that makes you great to be around.

MAINLY Cs

Hmmmm! You're a bit of a worrier. Try to think of the best possible outcome rather than the worst and see how much more fun you have!

WOULD YOU RATHER...

CIRCLE your CHOICES!

BE AN ASTRONAUT	OR	A ROCKET ENGINEER?
BE A ROCKSTAR	OR	A MUSIC PRODUCER?
BE A BLOGGER	OR	A VLOGGER
BE A DANCER	OR	A CHOREOGRAPHER?
BE A TRAIN DRIVER	OR	A BUS DRIVER?
BE A DOCTOR	OR	A DENTIST?
BE A NEWS HOST	OR	A WEATHER PRESENTER?
BE A FASHION DESIGNER	OR	A MODEL?
BE A WAITER	OR	A COOK?
BE A HAIRDRESSER	OR	A BEAUTICIAN?

PEDICURE

DRAW around your **TOES**, and then design an **AMAZING PEDICURE** for your **NAILS**.

MY MEGA
LIFE STORY

If a **FILM** was made about your **LIFE**, who would **PLAY** ...

YOU?

YOUR PARENTS?

YOUR BEST FRIEND?

YOUR FAVOURITE TEACHER?

WHAT WOULD THE FILM BE CALLED?

CHOOSE FIVE SONGS
FOR THE SOUNDTRACK.

3

1

4

2

5

3 EXCITING THINGS…

I've **ALREADY** done:

1 _____

2 _____

3 _____

I'd like to do **SOME DAY**:

1 _____

2 _____

3 _____

I've done this **MONTH**:

1 _____

2 _____

3 _____

103

ARE YOU A RISK-TAKER?

Answer the **QUESTIONS** and COLOUR a **SQUARE** for each **POINT** you score. When you have answered all the questions, find the **STAR** you are **CLOSEST** to for your **RESULT**.

START HERE

1 **HAVE YOU EVER RADICALLY CHANGED YOUR HAIRSTYLE?**
Yes (3)
No (1)

You like to play it safe and know what's around every corner.

2 **DO YOU ASK PEOPLE WHAT THEY WANT BEFORE YOU BUY THEM A GIFT?**
Sometimes (2)
Never (3)
Always (1)

3 **IF YOU SENT A VALENTINE, WOULD YOU ...**
sign your name? (4)
sign a fake name? (1)
leave it blank? (0)

You are naturally cautious, but you're prepared to take a risk if the reward is worth it.

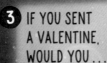

You're a natural risk-taker, but you know when to reject risks for a more predictable path!

16 17 18 19 20 21 22 23 24 15 14 13 12 11 10 9

6 WOULD YOU LET YOUR BFF PICK YOUR PROM OUTFIT?
Yes, definitely (3)
No way (1)
Maybe (2)

5 PICK ONE OF THE FOLLOWING JOBS:
Dog walker (2)
Pet groomer (1)
Crocodile keeper (4)
Horse trainer (3)

7 WOULD YOU APPEAR ON A REALITY TV SHOW?
Never (0)
Why not? (2)
Try and stop me! (3)

You can quickly assess a situation, and you know when to take a chance or run from risks.

4 HAVE YOU EVER PLANNED A SURPRISE PARTY FOR A FRIEND?
Yes, it was amazing! (4)
No, but I'd like to (2)
Yes, but never again! (1)

110% risk-taker! You have no fear and love the excitement of not knowing what will happen next!

AMAZING MAZE

FIND your way through the **HEART MAZE** to the **FINISH**.

START

FINISH

Can you SOLVE it in **UNDER** a MINUTE?

SILLY SENTENCE
:CHALLENGE:

Make as many **WORDS** as you can out of the LETTERS in this
SENTENCE without using a **LETTER** more than ●**NCE**.

_____   _____

_____   _____

_____   _____

_____   _____

_____   _____

_____   _____

_____   _____

Now, try and put those **WORDS** into a **SENTENCE**.

_____

_____

_____

_____

4 BOOKS THAT WOULD MAKE GREAT FILMS:

1 _____

2 _____

3 _____

4 _____

4 FILMS THAT WOULD MAKE GREAT STAGE SHOWS:

1 _____

2 _____

3 _____

4 _____

Scoop SEARCH

butterscotch caramel chocolate hazelnut

mint pistachio strawberry vanilla

t	w	m	c	v	e	k	f	g	b	c	v
c	y	b	u	o	t	g	o	j	u	b	h
a	v	x	h	o	i	m	i	n	t	x	a
r	g	i	y	b	a	v	i	v	t	y	z
a	q	k	r	m	t	y	n	e	e	r	e
m	s	t	r	a	w	b	e	r	r	y	l
e	v	a	n	i	l	l	a	u	s	r	n
l	h	z	a	u	t	n	f	z	c	q	u
g	p	i	s	t	a	c	h	i	o	s	t
r	a	j	c	h	l	a	e	g	t	y	h
k	r	t	k	m	g	g	w	m	c	y	v
c	h	o	c	o	l	a	t	e	h	a	c

Celebrity
►►► DOUBLES ◄◄◄

Pick a **FILM** or **SHOW** that **YOU** and your **FRIENDS** would be great in and **WRITE** it in the small boxes. Then, write the **CHARACTER** names in the left columns, and your and your friends' **NAMES** in the right columns.

_____ as _____

_____ as _____

_____ as _____

_____ as _____

_____ as _____

_____ as _____

_____ as _____

_____ as _____

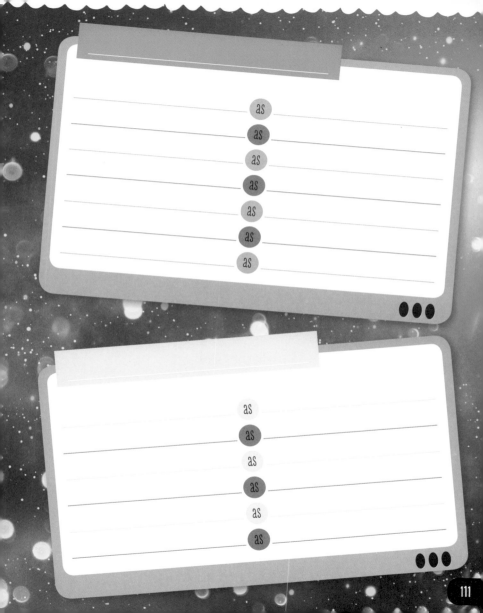

THEME PARK
designer

INVENT an awesome
THEME PARK RIDE.

WHAT'S IT CALLED? _____

BEST IN THE
:WORLD:

SINGER

MALE: _____

FEMALE: _____

ACTOR

MALE: _____

FEMALE: _____

AUTHOR

MALE: _____

FEMALE: _____

ATHLETE

MALE: _____

FEMALE: _____

ON A SCALE OF
ONE TO TEN
this is how much I'd like to ...

BUILD AN
ICE CASTLE /10

BE A HORSE
TRAINER /10

BE A TWIN /10

DESIGN MY
OWN CLOTHES /10

COMPETE IN
THE OLYMPICS /10

LIVE BY THE SEA /10

BE A SPY /10

BUILD A WEBSITE /10

AUDITION FOR A
TV TALENT SHOW /10

BE A TRIPLET /10

TOP 10

TV SHOWS:

1 _____
2 _____
3 _____
4 _____
5 _____
6 _____
7 _____
8 _____
9 _____
10 _____

YOUTUBE SHOWS:

1 _____
2 _____
3 _____
4 _____
5 _____
6 _____
7 _____
8 _____
9 _____
10 _____

BRILLIANT BREAK

CIRCLE **TEN WORDS** to create your dream **HOLIDAY**.

HOTEL

LAKE

MOUNTAINS

CASTLE

CRUISE

SWIMMING POOL

SAFARI

HOT TUB

SHIP

THEME PARK

JET SKI

DESERT ISLAND

TENT

THEATRE

MUSEUM

GO KARTING

JUNGLE

LOG CABIN

DESERT

ART GALLERY

CYCLING

TENNIS COURT

SNORKELLING

FOREST

SURFING

KARAOKE

SKIING

ROCK CLIMBING

BEACH

ROLLER DISCO

YACHT

QUAD BIKE

SNOW

CITY TOUR

SHOPPING

LANDMARKS

WATER PARK

HORSE RIDING

SUNSHINE

ICE-SKATING

COPYCORNS

COPY the **UNICORNS** onto the GRIDS.

Relatively
SPEAKING

Fill in this **SURVEY** about your **FAMILY**.

OLDEST PERSON:

YOUNGEST PERSON:

BEST COOK:

MOST UNUSUAL NAME:

BEST SINGER:

WORST SINGER:

BEST TEACHER:

BEST HOLIDAY PARTNER:

FUNNIEST PERSON:

SPORTIEST PERSON:

DESERT ISLAND

IMAGINE you are stranded on a **DESERT ISLAND** and then fill in the INFO.

FOUR things you would bring with you:

1 _____

2 _____

3 _____

4 _____

FOUR things you would **MISS** the most:

1 _____

2 _____

3 _____

4 _____

FOUR things you would need to build a **RAFT**:

1 _____

2 _____

3 _____

4 _____

FOUR things you would do to fill **TIME**:

1 _____

2 _____

3 _____

4 _____

FOUR things you would **BUILD** on the island:

1 _____

2 _____

3 _____

4 _____

WILL I EVER?

	I HOPE SO	MAYBE	NO WAY!
WALK A TIGHTROPE	☐	☐	☐
TAKE A BALLOON RIDE	☐	☐	☐
TAKE ACTING CLASSES	☐	☐	☐
HOLD A TARANTULA	☐	☐	☐
LEARN TO DRIVE A TRUCK	☐	☐	☐
DESIGN MY OWN CLOTHES	☐	☐	☐
LEARN TO DRIVE A TRAIN	☐	☐	☐
CHANGE THE COLOUR OF MY HAIR	☐	☐	☐
TRAIN A PUPPY	☐	☐	☐
LEARN TO FLY A PLANE	☐	☐	☐
DESIGN MY OWN HOUSE	☐	☐	☐
LEARN TO ROCK-CLIMB	☐	☐	☐

FIT FOR A Queen

DESIGN an OUTFIT for dinner with the QUEEN.

TOP 10

POP STARS:

1. _____
2. _____
3. _____
4. _____
5. _____
6. _____
7. _____
8. _____
9. _____
10. _____

BANDS:

1. _____
2. _____
3. _____
4. _____
5. _____
6. _____
7. _____
8. _____
9. _____
10. _____

World TOUR

CIRCLE five PLACES you'd LOVE to visit.

Taj Mahal

Loch Ness

Pantheon

Empire State Building

Great Wall of China

Eiffel Tower

Leaning Tower of Pisa

Tower of London

Pyramids

Uluru

Colosseum

Machu Picchu

Sydney Opera House

Zion National Park

The Great Barrier Reef

Mount Fuji

Buckingham Palace

The Louvre Museum

Golden Gate Bridge

La Sagrada Familia

3 FOODS
THAT TASTE BETTER WITH...

MUSTARD

1 _____

2 _____

3 _____

MAYONNAISE

1 _____

2 _____

3 _____

KETCHUP

1 _____

2 _____

3 _____

SPACE MISSION

If you were going to live in **SPACE** and could only take **FOUR** things from home, what would you **CHOOSE?**

1 _____

2 _____

3 _____

4 _____

Find the **THREE PLANETS** JUMBLED up in this SEQUENCE. All the **LETTERS** are in the **CORRECT** order.

JEMUAAPRITHRETSR

1 __ __ __ __ __ __

2 __ __ __ __ __

3 __ __ __ __ __ __ __

ANSWER the **QUESTIONS**, then total your As, Bs, and Cs.

1 YOUR FAVOURITE TV SHOW IS ABOUT TO START, BUT YOU HAVE AT LEAST AN HOUR'S HOMEWORK TO FINISH FOR TOMORROW. WHAT DO YOU DO?

A. Ditch the homework and watch TV. You can finish your fractions later.
B. Record the show and finish your homework.
C. Ask your mum and do what she says.

2 YOU ARE AUDITIONING FOR A PART IN YOUR SCHOOL PLAY AND HAVE JUST THREE DAYS LEFT TO LEARN YOUR LINES. DO YOU . . .

A. try to find time, but end up staying up late the night before the audition?
B. set aside some time each night to memorise your lines?
C. practise every night – but only if your friends offer to help you?

3 YOU'VE TRAINED HARD FOR MONTHS AND ACHIEVED THIRD PLACE IN THE SCHOOL SWIM-A-THON. DO YOU . . .

A. wonder if you could have come first if you'd trained a little harder?
B. continue practising and go for first place next year?
C. enter again next year, as long as your friends do?

4 WHEN YOU GOT YOUR FIRST PHONE, DID YOU . . .

A. only learn to text when people started sending you messages?
B. learn to text straight away?
C. wait for someone to offer to teach you how to text?

5 WHICH OF THESE SKILLS WOULD YOU LOVE TO LEARN THE MOST?

A. Multitasking (doing lots of things at once)
B. Speed-reading (reading a book in super quick time)
C. The art of persuasion – so you can get people to do things for you!

6 WHICH OF THESE IS MOST IMPORTANT IN A TRUE BFF?

A. Sense of adventure
B. Honesty
C. Support and encouragement

MAINLY As

You work hard but are easily distracted. You sometimes need a gentle nudge in the right direction, but more often than not you'll be happy with your achievements.

MAINLY Bs

If you're not giving 110%, you're giving something very close. Your fantastic focus means you're set to achieve your goals! Keep up the good work!

MAINLY Cs

It's not that you can't do something, it's that you just don't want to. It's a super casual outlook, but it won't give you a great sense of achievement.

DESIGN
YOUR OWN
LOGO

Your logo should be unique to you and say something about the kind of person you are. So think carefully about the shapes, colours and any words or pictures you use.

You can use your name, nickname or just initials. Remember to keep it simple so you can draw your logo again and again!

MUSIC PLAYLIST

WRITE the **NAME** of a **SONG** that makes you . . .

HAPPY

SAD

DANCE

SING

WRITE the **NAME** of a **SONG** that reminds you of . . .

MY BFF

MY FAMILY

Best OF THE YEAR

☑ the **BOX** next to your choice.

BEST SEASON:

Spring ☐   Summer ☐   Autumn ☐   Winter ☐

BEST MONTH:

January ☐   February ☐   March ☐   April ☐

May ☐   June ☐   July ☐   August ☐

September ☐   October ☐   November ☐   December ☐

TOP THREE DAYS OF THE YEAR:

1 _____

2 _____

3 _____

FOOD
FANATIC

Draw **THREE FOODS** you've **NEVER** tried but would **LIKE** to.

1

2

3

Draw **THREE FOODS** you've tried and **NEVER** want to again.

1

2

3

ON A SCALE OF
ONE TO TEN

this is how much I'd like to be a ...

DOCTOR	/10
	LIFEGUARD /10
JOURNALIST	/10
	WEBSITE DESIGNER /10
LIBRARIAN	/10
	POLICE OFFICER /10
PHOTOGRAPHER	/10
	TEACHER /10
JUDGE	/10
	FASHION DESIGNER /10

CELEBRITY SEARCH

Fill the **HEARTS** with the NAMES of your favourite **CELEBRITIES**.

Now, fill the **GRID** with these **NAMES**. Try to **LINK** the names **TOGETHER** like a **CROSSWORD PUZZLE** and then fill in the **BLANKS** with RANDOM LETTERS. Finally, CHALLENGE a FRIEND to **FIND** all the NAMES in the **WORDSEARCH!**

NAME-A-KITTEN

Think of CUTE NAMES for the KITTENS!

THREE...

COUNTRIES I would like to visit: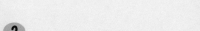

1 _____

2 _____

3 _____

CITIES I would like to visit:

1 _____

2 _____

3 _____

PLANETS I would like to visit:

1 _____

2 _____

3 _____

WOULD YOU RATHER...

CIRCLE your CHOICES!

WIN ONE GOLD MEDAL	**OR**	THREE BRONZE MEDALS?
BE AS TALL AS A HOUSE	**OR**	AS SMALL AS A MOUSE?
SING YOUR WORDS FOR A DAY	**OR**	SAY NOTHING AT ALL?
HAVE AN EXTRA EAR	**OR**	AN EXTRA NOSE?
LAUGH NON-STOP FOR A DAY	**OR**	SNEEZE NON-STOP FOR A DAY?
CLIMB A TREE	**OR**	SCALE A BUILDING?
HAVE NO BOOKS	**OR**	NO MUSIC?
LIVE ON A FARM	**OR**	IN A CASTLE?
WEAR YOUR MUM'S CLOTHES	**OR**	YOUR TEACHER'S CLOTHES?
SLEEP WITH YOUR LIGHT ON	**OR**	YOUR CURTAINS OPEN?

5 SKILLS
I WANT TO LEARN

1 _____
_____

2 _____
_____

3 _____
_____

4 _____
_____

5 _____
_____
_____

PAWFECT pets

ferret   gerbil   hamster   kitten

lizard   puppy   rabbit   turtle

q	p	o	d	z	g	y	r	n	b	z	h
p	k	l	o	x	m	f	e	r	r	e	t
h	i	i	p	v	v	s	o	j	w	z	x
o	t	r	u	r	a	b	b	i	t	g	m
m	t	c	p	z	s	d	k	n	r	l	g
c	e	q	p	i	j	h	a	r	b	i	e
f	n	u	y	o	x	a	z	u	s	z	r
c	z	t	w	t	c	m	t	u	w	a	b
q	o	v	c	k	u	s	p	a	n	r	i
t	u	r	t	l	e	t	b	f	x	d	l
b	x	k	u	p	h	e	b	j	y	e	f
d	o	z	n	b	j	r	i	e	r	t	r

:PHONE:

OF THE FUTURE

Think of **FIVE FUNCTIONS** that will make the **PHONE** of the **FUTURE AMAZING.**

1 _____

2 _____

3 _____

4 _____

5 _____

:Party TIME:

DESIGN a PARTY OUTFIT for your BFF.

DESIGN a PARTY
OUTFIT for YOURSELF.

3 things

I'm GREAT at:

1 _____

2 _____

3 _____

I want to LEARN:

1 _____

2 _____

3 _____

I need to TRY HARDER at:

1 _____

2 _____

3 _____

BRILLIANT BAKING

DESIGN your perfect CAKE.

WHAT FLAVOUR IS IT?

FANTASTIC FUTURE

Think of your **FRIENDS** in the **FUTURE**. WHO is **MOST** likely to . . .

BE A DOCTOR?

_____

BUILD THEIR OWN HOUSE?

_____

BE AN ARCHITECT?

_____

WIN A SPORTS MEDAL?

_____

BE AN ACTOR?

_____

WRITE A NOVEL?

_____

BE A JOURNALIST?

_____

TOUR THE WORLD?

_____

OWN A SHOP?

_____

BE IN A BAND?

_____

LIVE ABROAD?

_____

OWN A RESTAURANT?

_____

BE A YOUTUBE STAR?

_____

BE THE PRESIDENT?

_____

OWN A CAT SANCTUARY?

_____

WRITE A HIT SONG?

_____

DESIGN VIDEO GAMES?

_____

DREAM CAR

designer

DESIGN your
dream **CAR**.

MINI REVIEW

NAME: _____

☆☆☆☆☆

_____
_____
_____
_____
_____
_____
_____
_____
_____
_____
_____
_____
_____

WHAT KIND OF cupcake ARE YOU?

FOLLOW the **FLOW** and **FIND OUT.**

START

NEAT

MESSY

TV

BOOKS

HORSES

PUPPIES

ANIMALS

PEOPLE

SPORTS

ART

CINEMA

GALLERY

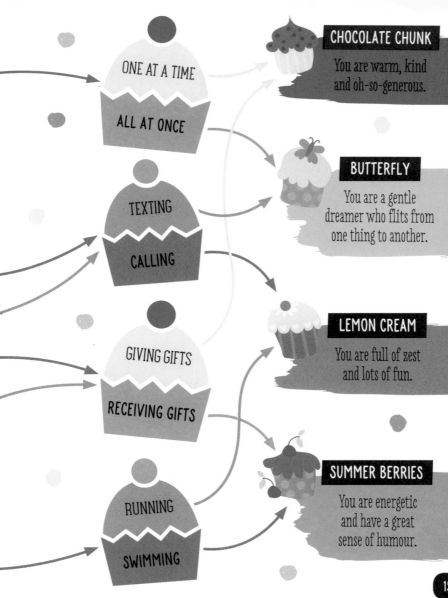

ONE AT A TIME

ALL AT ONCE

CHOCOLATE CHUNK
You are warm, kind and oh-so-generous.

TEXTING

CALLING

BUTTERFLY
You are a gentle dreamer who flits from one thing to another.

GIVING GIFTS

RECEIVING GIFTS

LEMON CREAM
You are full of zest and lots of fun.

RUNNING

SWIMMING

SUMMER BERRIES
You are energetic and have a great sense of humour.

:Emoti -ME:

HAPPY

_____

SAD

_____

ANNOYING

_____

BORING

_____

EXCITING

_____

EMBARRASSING

_____

SCARY

_____

SILLY

_____

3 THINGS
I'D DO IF I WERE...

A CAT

1 _____

2 _____

3 _____

A DOLPHIN

1 _____

2 _____

3 _____

A BIRD

1 _____

2 _____

3 _____

NEXT-DOOR
dreaming

WRITE your dream
NEIGHBOURS in the **HOUSES**.

ROYALTY
_____

POP STAR
_____

TV FAMILY
_____

ACTOR
_____

AUTHOR
_____

BOOK CHARACTER
_____

6

BOOK

Think of a **TITLE** for the **STORY** of your **LIFE**, then **DESIGN** the **COVER**.

WHAT'S IT CALLED?

THE **5** **BEST** THINGS ABOUT...

NAME: _____

1 _____

2 _____

3 _____

4 _____

5 _____

THE **5** **BEST**
THINGS ABOUT...

NAME:

1 _____

2 _____

3 _____

4 _____

5 _____

DESIGNER

DESIGN a **BAG** to carry
everything you need for a **HOLIDAY**.

AROUND THE *world*

CIRCLE the **FIVE COUNTRIES** you'd most like to **VISIT**.

France	China	Italy	Spain	Russia
Scotland	South Africa	Ireland	Canada	New Zealand
Japan	Australia	Thailand	Mexico	Germany
Egypt	Greece	India	Iceland	Norway
Brazil	England	Sweden	Poland	Belgium
Cyprus	Denmark	Peru	Hungary	Austria

WHAT'S YOUR STYLE?

FOLLOW the **FLOW** and **FIND OUT.**

START

DRESSES
JEANS

PARTY DRESS
BEACH DRESS

PONYTAIL
PLAITS

T-SHIRT
BLOUSE

SKINNY JEANS
BAGGY JEANS

CLUTCH BAG
SATCHEL

GIRLY COAT

LEATHER JACKET

PATTERNS

SEQUINS

HIGH HEELS

BAREFOOT

VINTAGE FIND

BRAND-NEW

STYLIN' SUPERSTAR

You love the latest fashions
and have a totally on-trend style!

GLITZY AND GLAM

You love dressing up and
being glamorous. Your style
always gets you noticed.

BARGAIN HUNTER

You are sale-rail savvy!
Your style makes for great
looks at low, low prices.

ONE OF A KIND

Your style is totally individual.
You love to rock your own look.

NOVEL ENDING

THINK of a **BOOK** you've enjoyed READING and make up an alternative ENDING.

NAME:

ALTERNATIVE ENDING:

school LIFE

TOP THREE CLASSES:

1. _____
2. _____
3. _____

TOP THREE TEACHERS:

1. _____
2. _____
3. _____

TOP THREE AFTER-SCHOOL CLUBS:

1. _____
2. _____
3. _____

3 THINGS

I'D DO IF I WERE...

as SMALL as a MOUSE:

1 _____

2 _____

3 _____

as TALL as a GIRAFFE:

1 _____

2 _____

3 _____

as FAST as a CHEETAH:

1 _____

2 _____

3 _____

WOULD YOU RATHER...

CIRCLE your CHOICES!

LEARN TAP DANCING	OR	BALLROOM DANCING?
LIVE ON A BEACH	OR	IN A FOREST?
WORK INDOORS	OR	WORK OUTDOORS?
FORGET YOUR LUNCH	OR	YOUR HOMEWORK?
BE GIVEN £1000 NOW	OR	£10 A WEEK FOR TEN YEARS?
WIN AN OSCAR	OR	AN OLYMPIC MEDAL?
WEAR A WIG MADE OF SPAGHETTI	OR	CANDYFLOSS?
BUILD A SNOWMAN	OR	A SANDCASTLE?
HAVE ROCK STAR PARENTS	OR	FILM STAR GRANDPARENTS?
BE A LIFEGUARD	OR	A SECURITY GUARD?

CHAIN REACTION

Find the **FIVE COLOUR WORDS** in this **SEQUENCE**. All the **LETTERS** are in the **CORRECT** order.

START →

P I N K P U R
P
L E Y N E E R G E L
L
O W O R A N G E

1 ___ ___ ___ ___

2 ___ ___ ___ ___ ___ ___

3 ___ ___ ___ ___ ___

4 ___ ___ ___ ___ ___ ___

5 ___ ___ ___ ___ ___ ___

168

Celebrity
PARTY

NAME FIVE CELEBRITIES YOU'D INVITE TO YOUR ULTIMATE BIRTHDAY PARTY:

1
2
3
4
5

WHICH BAND WOULD PLAY?

What **TYPE** of **CAKE** would you **SERVE**? **DRAW** it here. ⋙

AWARDS
CEREMONY

Think of **THREE NOMINATIONS** for each
CATEGORY, and then get your **FRIENDS** to VOTE.

FAVOURITE SHOW:

VOTES:

1 _____ _____

2 _____ _____

3 _____ _____

FAVOURITE AUTHOR:

VOTES:

1 _____ _____

2 _____ _____

3 _____ _____

FAVOURITE FILM:

VOTES:

1 _____ _____

2 _____ _____

3 _____ _____

FAVOURITE MUSICIAN:

VOTES:

1

2

3

FAVOURITE BOOK:

VOTES:

1 _____ _____

2 _____ _____

3 _____ _____

Host a **PARTY** to **ANNOUNCE** the **WINNERS**.

Birthday

SURPRISE

Think of **ALL** the **BIRTHDAY** GIFTS you have ever been **GIVEN** ...

WHAT WAS THE MOST UNUSUAL?

WHAT WAS THE MOST UNEXPECTED?

IS THERE ONE YOU'LL KEEP FOREVER?

Name **THREE INGREDIENTS** that would combine to make the **BEST ICE CREAM EVER.**

1 _____

2 _____

3 _____

SPORTS SEARCH

Find the **SPORTS NAMES** in the GRID.

- baseball
- basketball
- football
- golf
- hockey
- swimming
- tennis
- volleyball

m	t	e	g	b	k	b	p	s	h	k	h
e	i	j	o	a	c	z	q	t	d	e	n
k	a	x	l	s	h	n	s	u	y	q	b
d	u	o	f	k	v	z	j	x	f	l	a
v	o	l	l	e	y	b	a	l	l	v	s
v	e	k	t	t	h	o	c	k	e	y	e
p	m	j	e	b	y	h	z	j	m	t	b
v	z	e	n	a	u	t	z	g	q	o	a
w	y	c	n	l	o	v	u	g	e	j	l
s	m	i	i	l	a	m	j	j	k	r	l
y	p	y	s	f	o	o	t	b	a	l	l
c	i	y	s	w	i	m	m	i	n	g	x

▶▶▶ THRILLING ◀◀◀
INTERVIEW

WRITE SIX INTERVIEW QUESTIONS

1

2

3

4

5

6

WRITE your NAME at the top of one section
and your BFF'S **NAME** at the top of the other.
Then, **ANSWER** the QUESTIONS.

Do any of the **ANSWERS MATCH?**

LOL!

DESCRIBE the **FUNNIEST** thing that ever happened at SCHOOL.

ULTIMATE
ROCK BAND

LIST the **STARS** who would be in your **ULTIMATE BAND**.

1 _____
2 _____
3 _____
4 _____
5 _____

DESIGN a **LOGO** for the name of your BAND. »

EMOJI MAKER

DESIGN SIX new EMOJIS and NAME them.

IF I RULED THE
:WORLD:

Here are **FIVE THINGS** I'd do to make it even **BETTER!**

:Prickly:

PAIRS

180

WHAT'S THE...

FURTHEST you've
TRAVELLED?

_____

LATEST you've
GOT UP?

_____

LATEST you've
STAYED UP?

_____

HIGHEST you've
CLIMBED?

_____

FURTHEST you've
WALKED?

_____

LONGEST you've
STAYED AWAKE?

_____

ALPHA-NAME

Think of a BOY or GIRL'S NAME for every LETTER of the ALPHABET.

A _____
B _____
C _____
D _____
E _____
F _____
G _____
H _____
I _____
J _____
K _____
L _____
M _____

N _____
O _____
P _____
Q _____
R _____
S _____
T _____
U _____
V _____
W _____
X _____
Y _____
Z _____

MY MINI

magazine

Think of a **TITLE** for your own
MAGAZINE and DESIGN the **COVER**.

Prized
POSSESSIONS

WRITE down your **FIVE** most prized **POSSESSIONS.** Why are they **SPECIAL** to you?

1

2

3

4

5

MINI REVIEW

WRITE a mini REVIEW of the last **BOOK** you read.

TITLE: _____

☆☆☆☆☆

_____
_____
_____
_____
_____
_____
_____
_____
_____
_____
_____
_____
_____
_____
_____
_____
_____

Flag FUN

DESIGN a FLAG
for your TOWN.

DESIGN a **FLAG** for your **SCHOOL.**

DESIGN a **MASCOT** for your **SCHOOL.**

4 THINGS THAT WOULD MAKE YOUR BEDROOM A DREAM ROOM:

1 _____

2 _____

3 _____

4 _____

4 THINGS THAT YOU LOVE BEST ABOUT YOUR HOME TOWN:

1 _____

2 _____

3 _____

4 _____

PATCH PERFECTION

DESIGN FOUR PATCHES you would STITCH to your JACKET.

WHAT'S YOUR
MERMAID
NAME?

CIRCLE the first **LETTER** of your **NAME** in the PINK BOX and then circle the **MONTH** you were born in the YELLOW BOX.

A MELODY	**N** MERI	JANUARY	OCEAN
B ARIEL	**O** NIXIE	FEBRUARY	BUBBLE
C ZELDA	**P** OONA	MARCH	MOON
D VENUS	**Q** PEARL	APRIL	SEAFLOWER
E AZALEA	**R** CALYPSO	MAY	GEMSTONE
F SHELLY	**S** MARINA	JUNE	SHORE
G AQUA	**T** DOMINIQUE	JULY	SHIMMER
H CORAL	**U** SANDY	AUGUST	STARBURST
I DELPHIN	**V** FARIDAH	SEPTEMBER	STORM
J SERENA	**W** NERIDA	OCTOBER	SPARKLE
K JEWEL	**X** MURIEL	NOVEMBER	GLIMMER
L LUNA	**Y** IMOGEN	DECEMBER	DREAMER
M AMATHEIA	**Z** ISLA		

MY MERMAID NAME IS:

_____

_____

3 GREAT GADGETS

DRAW and name **THREE GADGETS** that would make your **LIFE** easier.

1 _____

_____

_____

_____

2 _____

_____

_____

_____

3 _____

_____

_____

_____

Super ME

If you were a **SUPERHERO**, what **POWERS** would you have? ☑ the **BOXES** and RATE each power as 'AWESOME!', 'NOT BAD', and '**RUBBISH!**'

	AWESOME!	NOT BAD	RUBBISH!
ABILITY TO FLY	☐	☐	☐
BEING INVISIBLE	☐	☐	☐
X-RAY VISION	☐	☐	☐
SUPERHUMAN STRENGTH	☐	☐	☐
TIME TRAVEL	☐	☐	☐
SHAPESHIFTING	☐	☐	☐
ABILITY TO READ MINDS	☐	☐	☐
LIVING FOREVER	☐	☐	☐
SUPERHUMAN SPEED	☐	☐	☐

DESIGN a **SUPERHERO** outfit.

WHAT WOULD YOUR SUPERHERO NAME BE?

MY SUPER COMIC

Fill the **PAGES** to create a **COMIC STRIP**. WRITE the **TITLE** of your **COMIC** in the first **BOX**.

THE END

MY MINI
CHALLENGES

Close your **EYES** and land your **FINGER** anywhere on the **PAGE**. Read the CLOSEST bubble and see if you can complete the **CHALLENGE!** ✓ the **BOX** when the challenge is COMPLETE.

DO 15 PRESS-UPS IN UNDER 2 MINUTES!

SAY THE ALPHABET BACKWARDS IN UNDER 60 SECONDS!

DO A FUNNY DANCE IN FRONT OF YOUR FRIENDS!

CROSS YOUR EYES AND CLICK YOUR FINGERS 10 TIMES!

STAND ON 1 LEG FOR A WHOLE MINUTE.

SAY THIS SENTENCE 10 TIMES WITHOUT MAKING A MISTAKE: "TEN TWINS TWIRLED TWELVE TWIGS." ☐

TRY LICKING YOUR ELBOW! ☐

DO 10 JUMPING JACKS IN UNDER 20 SECONDS! ☐

TAP YOUR HEAD AND RUB YOUR STOMACH WHILE SINGING YOUR FAVOURITE SONG! ☐

WHISTLE THE CHORUS TO YOUR FAVOURITE SONG. GET YOUR FRIENDS TO HUM THE BACKING TRACK. ☐

EAT A DOUGHNUT WITHOUT LICKING YOUR LIPS. ☐

TRY ROLLING YOUR TONGUE! ☐

SAY THIS SENTENCE TEN TIMES WITHOUT MAKING A MISTAKE: "BETTY BOTTER BOUGHT A BIT OF BUTTER." ☐

5 THINGS THAT WOULD MAKE YOUR DAY THE **BEST EVER!**

1 _____

_____

2 _____

_____

3 _____

_____

4 _____

_____

5 _____

_____

_____

FLOWER POWER

DRAW FLOWERS on the **PAGE** until it's FULL.

SUNSHINE *me*

WRITE the things that make you **HAPPIEST** inside the **SUN**.

Hot

OR NOT?

✓ the **BOX** for THINGS YOU think are **HOT** and
✗ the **BOX** for THINGS you think are **NOT**!

DENIM SHORTS	☐	BALLET FLATS	☐
CROCHET CARDIGANS	☐	FLUFFY BOOTS	☐
PLAYSUITS	☐	HIGH HEELS	☐
CROP TOPS	☐	COWBOY BOOTS	☐
MAXI DRESSES	☐	WEDGES	☐
HOODIES	☐	BIKER BOOTS	☐
BASEBALL CAPS	☐	PLAITS	☐
CHUNKY RINGS	☐	BLUE EYE SHADOW	☐
NEON BRACELETS	☐	CRIMPED HAIR	☐
BOW TIES	☐	FALSE NAILS	☐
PATTERNED SCARVES	☐	BLACK EYELINER	☐
HEADBANDS	☐	PINK NAIL POLISH	☐

MY DREAM DAY

CIRCLE your CHOICES to create your PERFECT day!

I WOULD EAT ...

FRUIT SALAD

FRENCH PASTRIES

EGGS, SAUSAGE, TOAST – THE WORKS

PANCAKE STACK

ICE CREAM

CEREAL

PIZZA

I WOULD WEAR ...

FANCY DRESS

PYJAMAS

JEANS AND A T-SHIRT

BEACH CLOTHES

A BALLGOWN

SPORTSWEAR

A CUTE DRESS

I WOULD BE ...

ON A BEACH

AT A SPA

ON A SHIP AT SEA

IN THE CITY

ON SAFARI

IN THE COUNTRY

IN A CASTLE

FIRST OF ALL, I WOULD ...

PLAY VIDEO GAMES

PAINT

WATCH A FILM

SUNBATHE

GO SWIMMING

THEN I WOULD ...

GO SKYDIVING

BAKE CAKES

GO TO A MUSICAL

PLAY A BOARD GAME

GO SHOPPING

AT THE END OF THE DAY, I WOULD ...

COOK A MEAL	WRITE IN MY DIARY	TAKE A NAP IN THE SOFTEST BED
SING AND DANCE	PLAY WITH KITTENS	HAVE A BIG MEAL
READ A BOOK	CHILL WITH FRIENDS	SIT BY A FIRE
HAVE A PARTY	GO TO A CONCERT	PLAY WITH PUPPIES

THE **5** **BEST**
THINGS ABOUT...

NAME:

1 _____

2 _____

3 _____

4 _____

5 _____

THE **5** **BEST**
THINGS ABOUT...

NAME: _____

1 _____

2 _____

3 _____

4 _____

5 _____

THE COLOUR OF MY HEART

Circle **FIVE WORDS** that contain the things you like **BEST**. Next, note which **COLOUR** you have chosen more of to see what the colour of your **HEART** says about you!

drama club

films

reading

choir

practical jokes

playing an instrument

crafts

girl guides

puzzles

volunteering

sleepovers

swimming

shopping

drawing

after-school clubs

concerts

poetry

team sports

parties

keeping a diary

camping

dancing

dog walking

theme parks

MAINLY PINK

You are loyal and dependable. People love spending time with you because you're always there for them.

MAINLY PURPLE

You are adventurous and always think of fun things to do. You can make anyone smile and are the life of any party.

MAINLY BLUE

You are caring, creative and like nothing more than giving thoughtful gifts, especially ones you made yourself. You can also write great stories and songs.

If you end up with two hearts of one colour and two of another, choose the word that best describes you and use the colour of its heart to reveal the colour of your heart.

FRIEND RINGS

WRITE the names of **FIVE FRIENDS** in the **BOXES**. In the **SPACES** where the **RINGS** cross over, **WRITE** one thing the owners of the RINGS have in common with **EACH OTHER**.

EXTRA STICKERS

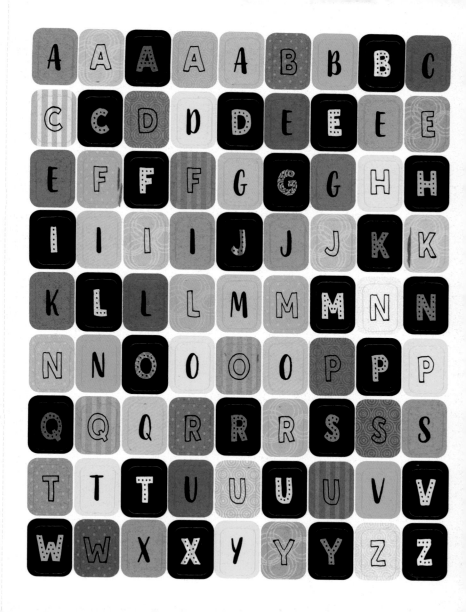